C000179235

Flute Exam Pieces

ABRSM Grade 2

Selected from the 2014–2017 syllabus

Piano accompaniment

Contents

Footnotes: Anthony Burton

The pieces in this album have been taken from a variety of different sources. Where appropriate, they have been checked with original source material and edited to help the player when preparing for performance. Ornament realizations have been added, as have the metronome marks shown within square brackets. Details of other editorial amendments or suggestions are given in the footnotes. Breath marks (retained here where they appear in the source edition) and all editorial additions are for guidance only; they are not comprehensive or obligatory. Descriptive titles are given in their original language, and translations into English appear above the footnotes.

ABRSM Flute Exams: requirements

Pieces

In the exam, candidates must play three pieces, one chosen from each of the three syllabus lists (A, B and C). Candidates are free to choose from the pieces printed in this album and/or from the other pieces set for the grade: a full list is given in the flute part with this score as well as in the 2014–2017 Woodwind syllabus.

Scales and arpeggios
Sight-reading
Aural tests
} Full details are available online at www.abrsm.org/flute2 or in the 2014–2017 Woodwind syllabus booklet.

First published in 2013 by ABRSM (Publishing) Ltd, a wholly owned subsidiary of ABRSM, 24 Portland Place, London W1B 1LU, United Kingdom
© 2013 by The Associated Board of the Royal Schools of Music

Music origination by Andrew Jones
Cover by Kate Benjamin & Andy Potts
Printed in England by Caligraving Ltd, Thetford, Norfolk

2

A:1

Que je chatouille ta fossette

from *Second livre de danceries*

Arranged by Ian Denley

attrib. Pierre Attaingnant
(c.1494–1551/2)

Que je chatouille ta fossette Let me tickle your dimple; **Second livre de danceries** Second Book of Dances

The galliard was a lively triple-time dance, probably of north Italian origin: its name is derived from the Italian word for 'vigorous'. The earliest printed galliards are to be found in the publications of Pierre Attaingnant, a pioneering printer of music in Paris. This example comes from his second volume of *Danceries*, a collection of dance tunes published in 1547. It is usually attributed to Attaingnant himself, but as far as is known he was not a composer, and he was probably responsible for the piece only as publisher and, perhaps, editor.

Minuetto

Arranged by Gilles Cagnard

Alessandro Scarlatti
(1660–1725)

Alessandro Scarlatti was born on the Italian island of Sicily, and spent most of his career in the two mainland cities of Rome and Naples. He was the father of the well-known keyboard composer Domenico Scarlatti. He composed more than 60 operas, setting the standard for the next generation of operatic composers, about 600 cantatas (smaller-scale vocal pieces for concert performance) and a good deal of church music. He also wrote for orchestra and for keyboard. Although the origin of this minuet is not entirely clear, in some sources it is identified as part of a toccata for organ or harpsichord.

Off She Goes

Arranged by Alan Bullard

Trad. Irish

Off She Goes is a traditional Irish jig, which like other folk tunes exists in many different versions. One version was recorded in a handwritten copy in the north-west of England in 1817; other versions have found their way to north America. Alan Bullard's arrangement (commissioned specially for this album) ends with a varied reprise of the first strain of the tune, including a stretched-out final phrase – notice the contrasts of dynamics here.

Boulevard Fanfarigoule

Hywel Davies
(born 1962)

Hywel Davies is a composer and sonic artist who lives in the west of England. As well as writing concert works and music for dance, he has created sound installations for outdoor and indoor locations, including one for the telephones of Arts Council England. This piece is named after a street familiar to the composer in La Napoule in the south of France. He suggests: 'Imagine pedalling your bicycle up the last hill before the sea: at bar 15 you reach the top and you can see the beach; then it's downhill all the way!'

February's Gentle Rain

from *A Flautist's Calendar*

Richard Kershaw
(born 1946)

Richard Kershaw was born in Leeds, in the north of England, and studied music at Oxford University. He taught for many years at Sherborne School in Dorset. *A Flautist's Calendar* is a collection of 12 pieces which depict the months of the year as described in a well-known children's poem by Sara Coleridge. This begins:

> January brings the snow,
> Makes our feet and fingers glow.
> February brings the rain,
> Thaws the frozen lake again.

You might imagine the piano's introduction to 'February's Gentle Rain' as representing the thawing lake and its offbeat accompaniment the falling rain, while the *cantabile* (singing) flute melody – later imitated by the piano – is more a suggestion of the feelings aroused by the thawing of the ice.

Reproduced by permission. All enquiries about this piece, apart from those directly relating to the exams, should be addressed to Pan Educational Music, 40 Portland Road, London W11 4LG.

Les feuilles mortes

Arranged by Peter Lawrance

Joseph Kosma (1905–69) and
Jacques Prévert (1900–77)

Les feuilles mortes Autumn Leaves

The French song *Les feuilles mortes*, with music by the Hungarian-born French composer Joseph Kosma and lyrics by the poet Jacques Prévert, was first heard in a 1946 film called *Les portes de la nuit*. The words are nostalgic, recalling a long-ago love affair. In 1947 the American songwriter Johnny Mercer wrote an English version under the title *Autumn Leaves*. The chorus begins:

> The falling leaves drift by the window,
> The autumn leaves of red and gold.

In this form, the song became a best-selling recording for several singers, and a jazz 'standard' – a well-known basis for improvisation. This arrangement by Peter Lawrance is reproduced from his book *Winner Scores All* (published by Brass Wind).

Flute Exam Pieces

ABRSM Grade 2

Selected from the 2014–2017 syllabus

Name	
Date of exam	

Contents

page

Footnotes: Anthony Burton

Other pieces for Grade 2

First published in 2013 by ABRSM (Publishing) Ltd, a wholly owned subsidiary of ABRSM, 24 Portland Place, London W1B 1LU, United Kingdom © 2013 by The Associated Board of the Royal Schools of Music

Music origination by Andrew Jones
Cover by Kate Benjamin & Andy Potts
Printed in England by Caligraving Ltd, Thetford, Norfolk

MIX
Paper from responsible sources
FSC™ C109619

Que je chatouille ta fossette

from *Second livre de danceries*

Arranged by Ian Denley

attrib. Pierre Attaingnant
(c.1494–1551/2)

Que je chatouille ta fossette Let me tickle your dimple; **Second livre de danceries** Second Book of Dances

The galliard was a lively triple-time dance, probably of north Italian origin: its name is derived from the Italian word for 'vigorous'. The earliest printed galliards are to be found in the publications of Pierre Attaingnant, a pioneering printer of music in Paris. This example comes from his second volume of *Danceries*, a collection of dance tunes published in 1547. It is usually attributed to Attaingnant himself, but as far as is known he was not a composer, and he was probably responsible for the piece only as publisher and, perhaps, editor.

© 1998 by The Associated Board of the Royal Schools of Music
Reproduced from *Time Pieces for Flute*, Volume 2, selected and arranged by Ian Denley (ABRSM)

Minuetto

A:2

Arranged by Gilles Cagnard

Alessandro Scarlatti
(1660–1725)

Alessandro Scarlatti was born on the Italian island of Sicily, and spent most of his career in the two mainland cities of Rome and Naples. He was the father of the well-known keyboard composer Domenico Scarlatti. He composed more than 60 operas, setting the standard for the next generation of operatic composers, about 600 cantatas (smaller-scale vocal pieces for concert performance) and a good deal of church music. He also wrote for orchestra and for keyboard. Although the origin of this minuet is not entirely clear, in some sources it is identified as part of a toccata for organ or harpsichord.

A:3

Off She Goes

Arranged by Alan Bullard

Trad. Irish

Off She Goes is a traditional Irish jig, which like other folk tunes exists in many different versions. One version was recorded in a handwritten copy in the north-west of England in 1817; other versions have found their way to north America. Alan Bullard's arrangement (commissioned specially for this album) ends with a varied reprise of the first strain of the tune, including a stretched-out final phrase – notice the contrasts of dynamics here.

Boulevard Fanfarigoule

Hywel Davies
(born 1962)

Hywel Davies is a composer and sonic artist who lives in the west of England. As well as writing concert works and music for dance, he has created sound installations for outdoor and indoor locations, including one for the telephones of Arts Council England. This piece is named after a street familiar to the composer in La Napoule in the south of France. He suggests: 'Imagine pedalling your bicycle up the last hill before the sea: at bar 15 you reach the top and you can see the beach; then it's downhill all the way!'

February's Gentle Rain

from *A Flautist's Calendar*

Richard Kershaw
(born 1946)

Richard Kershaw was born in Leeds, in the north of England, and studied music at Oxford University. He taught for many years at Sherborne School in Dorset. *A Flautist's Calendar* is a collection of 12 pieces which depict the months of the year as described in a well-known children's poem by Sara Coleridge. This begins:

> January brings the snow,
> Makes our feet and fingers glow.
> February brings the rain,
> Thaws the frozen lake again.

You might imagine the piano's introduction to 'February's Gentle Rain' as representing the thawing lake and its offbeat accompaniment the falling rain, while the *cantabile* (singing) flute melody – later imitated by the piano – is more a suggestion of the feelings aroused by the thawing of the ice.

Les feuilles mortes

Arranged by Peter Lawrance

Joseph Kosma (1905–69) and
Jacques Prévert (1900–77)

Les feuilles mortes Autumn Leaves

The French song *Les feuilles mortes*, with music by the Hungarian-born French composer Joseph Kosma and lyrics by the poet Jacques Prévert, was first heard in a 1946 film called *Les portes de la nuit*. The words are nostalgic, recalling a long-ago love affair. In 1947 the American songwriter Johnny Mercer wrote an English version under the title *Autumn Leaves*. The chorus begins:

> The falling leaves drift by the window,
> The autumn leaves of red and gold.

In this form, the song became a best-selling recording for several singers, and a jazz 'standard' – a well-known basis for improvisation. This arrangement by Peter Lawrance is reproduced from his book *Winner Scores All* (published by Brass Wind).

Austrian Allure

C:1

Ian Denley
(born 1952)

Ian Denley studied flute and piano at the Royal Northern College of Music in Manchester, and for many years has taught flute at the University of Hull, and woodwind instruments at various schools in East Yorkshire in the north of England. His publications include collections of educational pieces and a two-part tutor called *Flute Time*. The first volume includes this study in the time of the Austrian dance, a precursor of the waltz, called the ländler.

© Oxford University Press 2003
Reproduced by permission. All enquiries about this piece, apart from those directly relating to the exams, should be addressed to Oxford University Press, Great Clarendon Street, Oxford OX2 6DP.

Waltzlet

from *The Modern Flute Player*

Mike Mower
(born 1958)

Mike Mower was born in Bath, in the west of England, and studied the flute at the Royal Academy of Music in London. He has written many educational pieces which aim, he says, 'to bridge the gap between classical and jazz music', and which are 'in different musical styles, … challenging, but always tuneful and enjoyable to play'. This 'Waltzlet' adds to the usual *one*–two–three of waltz time some syncopations typical of jazz; observing the markings for tenuto and staccato will help you get the right feeling. Although the composer's metronome mark is ♩ = 152, students may prefer a more relaxed tempo of ♩ = *c.*138.

© by Itchy Fingers Publications

Reproduced by permission. All enquiries about this piece, apart from those directly relating to the exams, should be addressed to Itchy Fingers Publications, 10 Warminster Road, Beckington, Somerset, BA11 6SY.

C:3

Study in D

No. 69 from *Schule für die Böhm-Flöte*, Op. 7, Part 1

Edited by Immanuel Lucchesi

Emil Prill
(1867–1940)

Schule für die Böhm-Flöte Method for the Boehm Flute

Emil Prill was a German flautist, born in Stettin (now Szczecin in Poland). He studied in Berlin, taught the flute in Russia, and played in orchestras in Hamburg and Berlin; from 1903 to 1934 he was professor of flute at the Royal High School for Music in Berlin. Prill published a flute method, numerous sets of studies, and a guide to the flute repertoire listing over 7500 works. This is a study in smooth, expressive phrasing, in which one of the challenges is to find the right places to breathe. Don't let the scarcity of dynamic markings prevent you shaping it in your own way.